JANET AND JOHN

BOOK

BY

MABEL O'DONNELL A

ILLUSTRATED BY
FLORENCE AND MARGARET HOOPES

JAMES NISBET AND CO. LTD.
DIGSWELL PLACE

walked   **what**

I walked and walked
and what did I see?

saw Puppy

I saw Little Puppy
and he saw me.
Little Puppy ran.
He ran to me.

I walked and walked
and what did I see?

I saw little kittens.

One, two, three.

" Come here," I said.

" Come here to me."

I walked and walked
and what did I see ?

with

I saw John
and John saw me.
" Come and play," he said.
" Come and play with me."

I walked and walked
and what did I see?

home   she

I saw Mother
and Mother saw me.
" Come home," she said.
" Come home with me."

trains

John said,

"I like big trains.

I like little trains.

I can see a big train.

I like to ride in trains."

There   day

John said,

"There is a big ship.

Here is my little boat.

I like to ride in big ships.

I like to play with little boats.

One day I will go in a big ship."

have   high

John said,

" I like aeroplanes.

I want to go up in an aeroplane.

One day I shall have a ride

in a big aeroplane.

I shall go up high in an aeroplane."

her   was

Janet sat in the sun.

Her doll was on her lap.

Mother was on the step.

"See what I have," said Mother.

dear   brown

It was a puppy.

Mother held him on her lap.

Janet said,

"What a dear little puppy.

What a soft brown puppy."

"Look, Mother," said Janet.
"He is a dear little puppy.
But he just sits still.

I want him to run and play.
Will he play with me?"

Janet saw Father.

She ran to Father and said,

"Look at this dear little puppy.

I want him to run and play.

But he just sits still.

May I have him for a pet?"

call

"Yes," said Father.

"You may have the little puppy."

"Thank you," said Janet.

"I will call him Scot.

Look, Scot can jump.

See him jump up at my dress."

seen

Janet said to Mother,

"May I go and play with Jill?

Scot will come with me.

Jill has not seen him yet."

"Yes. You may go," said Mother.

"Thank you," said Janet.

We leaves trees

"Come with me, Scot," said Janet.
"We must go and see Jill."
Janet walked and walked.
The little dog went with her.
The leaves fell from the trees.

new

Janet and Scot met Jill.

"Come with us, Jill," said Janet.

"Look at my new brown puppy.

He runs after the leaves in the wind."

Jill said,

" What a dear little puppy.

I like the new brown puppy."

Scot still ran after the leaves.

The leaves still fell from the trees.

" What shall we play ? " said Jill.

" Shall we play with the sand ?
Scot can dig in the sand."

" Let us go to the pond," said Janet.

" We can see the fish swim."

swing

"I like the sand," said Jill.

"I like the pond.

But I like the swing best.

Let us go and play on the swing."

"Yes," said Janet.
"I like the swing too."
Janet went on the swing.
She went up and down.
The swing went high,
and Janet held on.

"I went very high," said Janet.

"I had a good swing.

I shall stop and get off.

You must have a swing next."

"Thank you," said Jill.

"I like to go on the swing.

I like to go high."

Do   please

John went to see a big aeroplane.

The man in the aeroplane said,

"Do you want to come with me?"

"Yes, please," said John.

"I want to come with you."

" Jump in," said the man.

Father and John got in.

Mother stood with the puppy.

" Good-bye, Mother," said John.

" Here we go," said the man.

are

The aeroplane went up fast.

"We are off," said John.

"What a good ride!

I like to fly in an aeroplane."

looked　houses　be

The aeroplane went up high.

John looked down.

He saw houses.

He saw a ship.

He saw trees.

But he did not see Mother.

"We must be too high," said John.

Down went the aeroplane,

down, down, down.

John saw houses. John saw trees.

Soon John saw Mother.

"Look, Father," said John.

"We have come back.

There is Mother."

John ran to meet Mother.

"It was a good ride," he said.

"But I am glad we are back."

Jill said,

" Come to my house.

You have not seen my new kittens."

Janet said,

" I must send Scot home.

He will want to catch the kittens.

Go home, Scot ! Go home ! "

Oh   were   they

There were three new kittens.

"Oh, Jill," said Janet,

"They are good little kittens.

Is this the kittens' bed?

Do they sleep in this box?"

into

Scot ran into the room.

" Quick, Janet," said Jill.

" Catch Scot and keep him.

I will catch the kittens.

I will pick them up."

Janet held the puppy.

Jill stood with the kittens.

"Keep still, Scot," said Janet.

"You must not run after the kittens.

They do not want to play.

You must come home with me.

Good-bye, Jill.   Good-bye."

put   coat   small   Teddy

Janet put on her brown coat.

It was very small.

"This coat will not do," said Janet.

"Look, Teddy. It is much too small."

Janet ran to Mother.

"Look at my brown coat," she said.

"It is much too small for me.

I am too big for this brown coat."

Mother and Janet and Teddy
went to the shop.

At the shop Mother said,
"Janet's coat is too small.
She must have a new coat."

"I am too big for this coat," said Janet.
"I want a red coat, please."

blue

There were coats and coats and coats.

There were brown coats.

There were blue coats.

There were green coats.

Janet stood and looked.

"I can not see a red coat," she said.

Janet looked and looked.

She saw a green coat.

She saw brown coats.

She saw blue coats.

"They are good coats," Janet said.

"But I wish I had a red coat."

Mother looked for a red coat.

"Look here, Janet," said Mother.

"Here is a red coat.

Let us see if it fits you."

Janet put on the red coat.

"It fits me very well," said Janet.

"Look, Teddy. Look at my new coat."

Janet and John went to the shop.

John's big dog went with them.

But the little dog ran off.

"Come here, Scot," said Janet.

The puppy did not stop.

He ran on and on.

came   hole   out

Scot ran till he came to a big hole.
He did not see it. He fell in.

It was a very deep hole.

Scot was too small to jump out.
He was a sad little dog.
He was lost in the hole.

Janet and John came back.

They had a basket.

The big dog held a bag in his teeth.

The little dog was not there.

Janet said,

"Scot, Scot, come here!"

But Scot did not come.

where   find

"Oh, John," said Janet,
"I think Scot must be lost.
Where can he be?"
John said,
"My big dog will find him.
He will bring Scot back."
The big dog ran off.
Janet and John ran after him.

The big dog soon came to the hole.

"There is Scot," said John.

"He is down in the hole.

It is too steep for him to get out."

Janet said,

"Poor little Scot,

Let us lift him out."

Scot was glad.

He was out of the hole.

toy

One day John went into a toy shop.

He saw the toys on a shelf.

He saw a blue boat on the shelf.

"I like that boat," said John.

better

Then he saw a red train.

It was next to the blue boat.

John looked at the red train.

"I like the red train better," he said.

ball

John looked at the toys.

He saw a cat with black spots.

He saw a big brown ball.

A small red jug stood next.

Then came a little man in blue.

At the end was an aeroplane.

John said,

"I like the aeroplane best."

The aeroplane had red wings.

The rest of it was black.

John looked at the toys.

He saw a red Jack-in-the-box.

He saw two queer dogs.

He saw a man with his hand out.

"Yes, yes," said John.

"They are very good toys,

but the aeroplane can fly."

pat	jam	fan	sat	van
lap	man	bag	cap	has

hen	red	men	leg	bed
set	ten	get	yes	pet

win	dig	lid	six	big
sit	him	pig	kid	dip

hop	got	box	not	dog
top	fog	dot	sob	hot

bud	fun	sum	cup	but
run	nut	bun	dug	cub

add	moss	bell	kiss	doll
less	well	miss	puff	buzz

back	sock	duck	kick	lock
neck	pick	lack	rock	sick
ship	shed	shell	ash	rush
shop	shot	dish	wish	fish
shut	shall	cash	hush	dash
crab	drag	flag	frog	grin
cram	drum	flat	from	grab
crop	dress	fled	frill	grub
plum	skin	slip	snug	spot
plan	skip	slap	snap	spin
plug	skid	slam	sniff	spill
stem	swim	trip	twig	blot
stop	swam	tram	twin	bless
stud	swum	trot	bran	bred

glad	clock	still	black	smash
gruff	prop	cross	crush	trick
brick	flash	smell	stick	frock

must	best	soft	lost	held
lift	self	west	send	rest
wind	just	hand	left	milk

melt	camp	tops	kept	grand
jump	help	sits	next	spend
desk	went	buns	dolls	swift

bee	see	tree	feet	sweet
need	week	deep	sheep	sheet
keep	feel	meet	creep	green

| too | cool | soon | boot | spoon |
| food | moon | roof | broom | stool |

book	wool	cook	look	shook
good	foot	wood	brook	stood

queen	queer	quick	quilt	quack

chin	chat	chip	chick	cheek
chop	chum	chill	cheer	chest
much	such	catch	witch	inch
rich	beech	fetch	match	lunch

than	that	this	then	them
thin	thud	thick	three	thrush
with	moth	cloth	tooth	teeth

Revision

luck	crept	frost	spell	tramp
glee	pond	black	hatch	droop
dust	crash	thump	shelf	grunt

when	whip	wheel	which	whisk

ink	tank	rank	drink	think
bank	pink	plank	trunk	thank
sunk	wink	sink	blank	blink

king	long	bring	thing	spring
sang	rung	strung	clang	strong
hung	bang	swing	wing	string

Revision

trap	brush	lung	stuck	quill
land	link	sweep	crust	sling
silk	print	clank	shoot	crack

Revision

bend	drank	stand	gong	brick
pack	elf	clung	hunt	prank
just	flock	trick	press	whisk

PRINTED IN GREAT BRITAIN BY MORRISON AND GIBB LTD., LONDON AND EDINBURGH
(S 1780)